THE MAHABHARATA
CHILDREN'S ILLUSTRATED CLASSICS

THE MAKING of GREAT WARRIORS

Retold by **CHARU AGARWAL DHANDIA**
Art **KAVITA SINGH KALE** *Design* **RACHITA RAKYAN**

Published by
Rupa Publications India Pvt. Ltd 2020
7/16, Ansari Road, Daryaganj
New Delhi 110002

Sales centres:
Allahabad Bengaluru Chennai
Hyderabad Jaipur Kathmandu
Kolkata Mumbai

Edition copyright © Rupa Publications Pvt. Ltd 2020

All rights reserved.
No part of this publication may be reproduced, transmitted,
or stored in a retrieval system, in any form or by any means, electronic, mechanical, photocopying,
recording or otherwise,
without the prior permission of the publisher.

ISBN: 978-81-291-4969-5

First impression 2020

10 9 8 7 6 5 4 3 2 1

The moral right of the author has been asserted.

Printed at Nutech Print Services - India

This book is sold subject to the condition that it shall not, by way of trade or otherwise, be lent, resold, hired out, or otherwise circulated, without the publisher's prior consent, in any form of binding or cover other than that in which it is published.

Charu Agarwal Dhandia weaves together her two biggest passions—studying Indian classical literature and creative storytelling. She is an economist by training and works in the social development space.

Kavita Singh Kale's background as an artist and a designer enables her to draw a thin line between design following functionality and pure self-expression. This has helped her evolve as a transmedia artist. Her work includes art installations, children's books, comics, paintings and videos.

Rachita Rakyan combines over 15 years of expertise in graphic design and art direction with deep understanding of functionality and aesthetics across print, publishing, branding and digital media.

CONTENTS

KURU DYNASTY	*IV-V*
KEY CHARACTERS	*VI-VII*
SHANTANU AND GANGA	1
VASHISHTHA'S CURSE	15
DEVAVRATA AND SATYAVATI	21
AMBA	33
VYASA'S BOONS	45

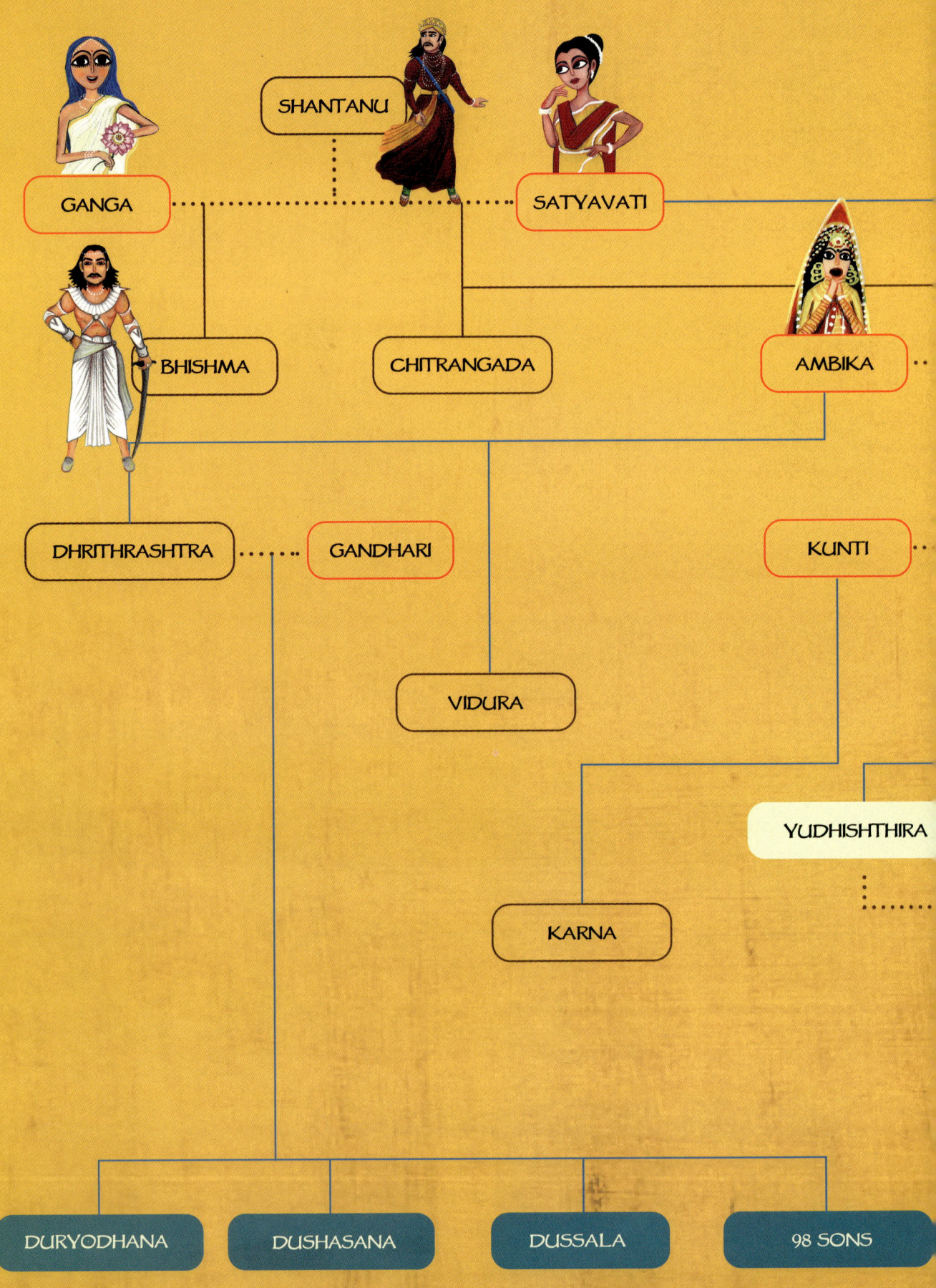

KURU DYNASTY

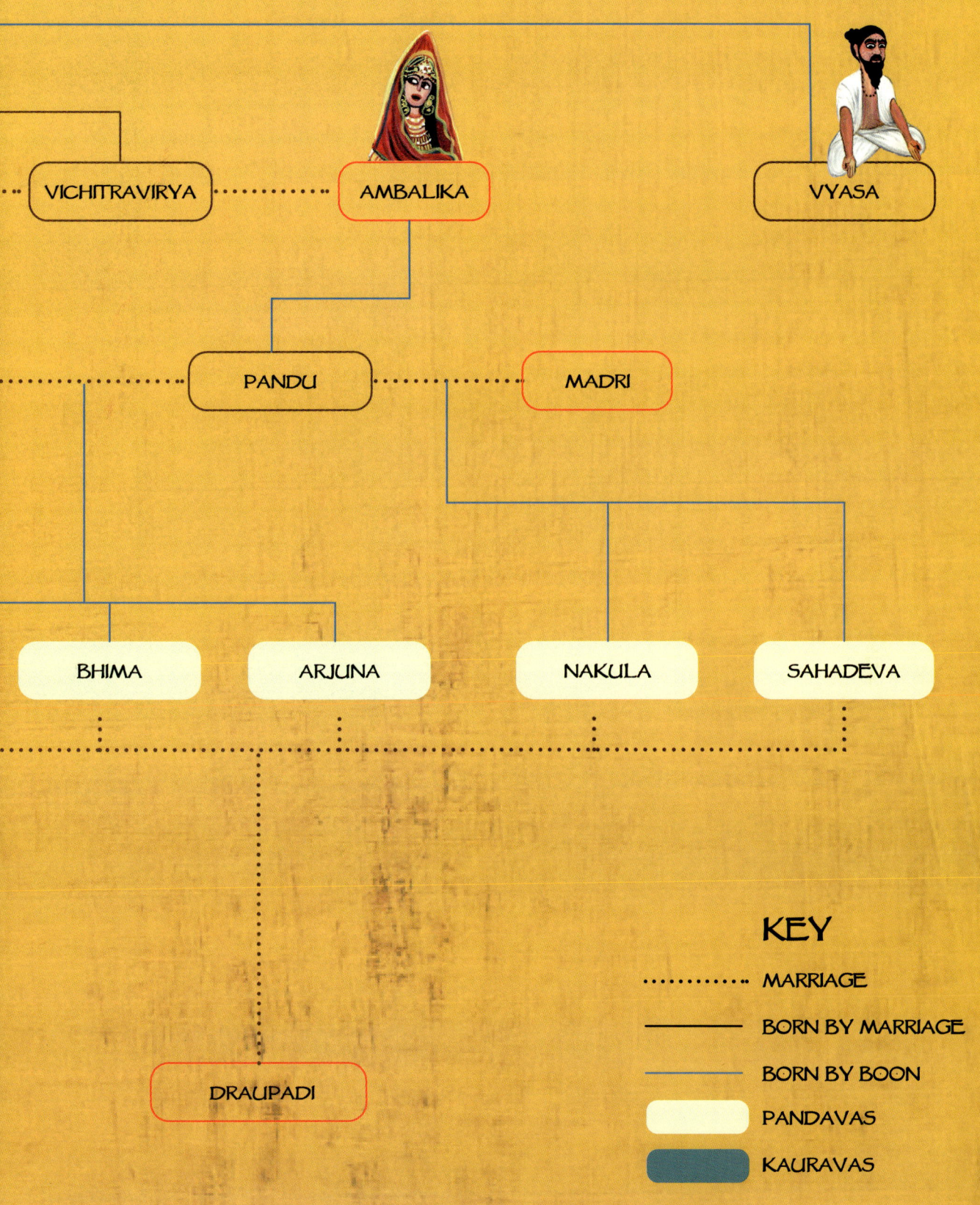

KEY CHARACTERS

SHANTANU

King of Hastinapur who married Ganga and later Satyavati. He was the father of the fearless Devavrata and princes Chitrangada and Vichitravirya.

GANGA

Enchanting and beautiful goddess of the sacred river Ganga. She descended to earth as a beautiful woman to honour the curse of sage Vashishtha on eight Vasus. She married King Shantanu and gave birth to Devavrata.

BHISHMA

Born as Devavrata to King Shantanu and Goddess Ganga, he came to be known as Bhishma, meaning 'the firm.' He was an unparalleled archer and the greatest warrior of that time.

SATYAVATI

Daughter of the chief of fishermen Dusharaj, Satyavati was a beautiful maiden who would ferry people in her boat. She was married to Shantanu and gave birth to sons Chitrangada and Vichitravirya. She was also mother to the mighty sage Vyasa.

VYASA

The immortal sage who composed the Mahabharata. Vyasa was born to Satyavati. Later he gave boons for the birth of Dhrithrashtra, Pandu and the hundred Kaurava brothers.

AMBA

The eldest daughter of the King of Kashi, She was abducted by Bhishma. Amba was very angry with Bhishma and wanted to take revenge. She prayed to Shiva and got a boon.

SHANTANU AND GANGA

Many years ago, there lived Shantanu, the King of Hastinapur. Shantanu was a great hunter, known for being wise and brave.

One sunny morning, Shantanu went out to hunt in the forest. On the banks of river Ganga, he saw a beautiful young lady coming out of the water. The golden sun fell on her bright face. She was Goddess Ganga in a gorgeous human form.

Shantanu fell in love with Ganga at once. He said, 'Who are you? I am the King of Hastinapur and I want to marry you!'

Ganga smiled and replied, 'Dear King, I will marry you. But before that, I have two conditions. I will become your queen only if you promise to follow them as long as we are married.'

Shantanu listened carefully to Ganga's conditions. Ganga said, 'My first condition is that no one will ever ask me who I am and where I have come from. Second, no one must ever try to stop me from doing anything. Do not say anything nasty to me or I will leave you and go away.'

Shantanu accepted both the conditions and married Ganga. They went back to Hastinapur and began living together happily.

A few months passed and Ganga gave birth to a baby boy. On hearing the news, Shantanu was overjoyed! He rushed to the palace to meet Ganga and their newborn son. On reaching his chambers, Shantanu saw Ganga leaving the palace with the baby in her arms.

Ganga was going towards the river. Shantanu was curious to know what she was doing and followed her. On reaching the river bank, Shantanu was shocked to see Ganga leaving the baby in the water!

Shantanu was deeply saddened and felt miserable but he could not ask Ganga anything. He was bound by his promise to her.

Ganga kept repeating this for a few years, while Shantanu remained helpless. One morning, Ganga was again taking her newborn son to the river. Shantanu saw Ganga from his window and rushed out to stop her.

This time, he lost his patience. He held Ganga by her arm and cried, 'Stop, Queen! Why are you doing this? I demand to know!'

Hearing this, Ganga replied, 'Oh no! You have broken your promise. I cannot stay with you any longer. But before I leave, I will tell you why I drowned our sons. It is a secret I have carried with me for many years.'

VASHISHTHA'S CURSE

Shantanu and Ganga sat on the river bank. Staring at the rushing water, Ganga began narrating the story of Nandini and the eight Vasus.

Rishi Vashishtha was a great sage. He lived in the forest with his cow Nandini. Nandini was no ordinary cow. She was called the 'Cow of Plenty'. She had the power to grant wishes to her owner.

One day, eight Vasus were walking in the woods when they saw Nandini grazing under a tree. Dyu was the wisest of the Vasus. His wife pulled his arm and said, "Look, that's the magical Nandini! Let's take her with us!" The other Vasus tried to stop Dyu's wife but she refused to listen and insisted on taking Nandini.

So the Vasus untied Nandini and started walking away with her. Meanwhile, Vashishtha returned and could not find Nandini anywhere. This made Vashishtha furious! He shut his eyes and used his divine powers to find her.

"The Vasus have committed a great sin. They have stolen a hermit's cow. They have to be punished!" thought Vashishtha angrily.

"I curse the Vasus to be born as humans in their next birth and live on earth!" said Vashishtha.

The Vasus heard Vashishtha's curse. They rushed to him and pleaded him to take the curse back. Vashishtha said, "Since you are sorry for what you did, I will punish only Dyu to live on earth for his entire life. He will become a great warrior but he will remain childless. The rest of you will come back in a day."

Ganga continued, 'I was sent to you by the Vasus. I took a human form to marry you and give birth to the eight Vasus, each for only one day.' Shantanu listened quietly.

Ganga continued, 'My purpose is now over and I must go back to heaven. I am taking our son with me. But I promise to bring him back to you when he is grown up.' Saying this, Ganga disappeared into the river with the baby in her arms. Shantanu was left sad and miserable. Alone, he returned to his palace.

DEVAVRATA AND SATYAVATI

A few years passed. Every day, Shantanu would sit by the river and think of Ganga and their son. One such morning, Shantanu saw a woman coming out of the river. It was Ganga! This time Ganga had not come alone. There was a young handsome boy with her. Ganga came closer to Shantanu and said, 'Dear King, I have kept my promise. This is your son, Devavrata. He has grown into a young and brave warrior. He is ready to become the king!'

Shantanu's happiness knew no bounds! He finally had his son back. Shantanu held Devavrata in his arms and hugged him. Together, they walked back to the palace. Soon, Shantanu crowned Devavrata as the Prince of Hastinapur.

Devavrata or Bhishma, as he was later called, became the most skilled warrior in Hastinapur.

Devavrata was brave and wise, just like Shantanu. Everyone wanted him to be the king of Hastinapur.

One day, when Shantanu was walking by the river, he found a strange sweet fragrance in the air. He wanted to find out where it was coming from. He followed it and reached a small hut made of wood and dry leaves. He opened the door. There was a beautiful young girl inside. The fragrance was coming from her! She was sitting with her old father.

Shantanu asked, 'Who are you, young lady?'
'I am Satyavati. I ferry holy men from one bank of the river to the other in my boat. I live with my father Dusharaj, the chief of fishermen,' replied Satyavati. Shantanu fell in love with the sweet-smelling Satyavati. He turned to Dusharaj and said, 'I want to marry your daughter.'

Dusharaj said, 'I will let you marry my daughter but I have a condition. You will have to crown Satyavati's son as the king.'

Shantanu loved Devavrata dearly and had prepared him to be the king. So he told Satyavati's father that he could not agree to the condition and returned to his palace.

Months passed. Shantanu kept thinking of Satyavati and became sad. He lost all interest in his kingdom. Devavrata loved his father and wanted to know why Shantanu was so troubled. One day, he came to know of Satyavati.

Devavrata secretly went to meet Dusharaj. He said, 'Sir, I accept your condition on behalf of my father Shantanu. I assure you that Satyavati's son will rule Hastinapur. Please let my father marry Satyavati.'

Dusharaj replied, 'I trust you, prince. But how do I know that your children will keep your promise?'

Devavrata thought for a moment and said, 'I will have no children. I pledge never to marry.' Because of this promise, Devavrata came to be known as Bhishma, 'the firm'. His sacrifice for his father became an example to all.

Bhishma returned to the palace and in a few days, Shantanu married Satyavati.

AMBA

Satyavati gave birth to two sons, Chitrangada and Vichitravirya. But soon their father Shantanu passed away. Chitrangada and Vichitravirya were still very young. But keeping Dusharaj's condition, Chitrangada was made the new king.

In a few days, Chitrangada died in a war. Vichitravirya, who was very young at that time, became the King of Hastinapur. Bhishma became his guardian.

King Kashya of Kasi announced a *swayamvar* to choose husbands for his three daughters—Amba, Ambika and Ambalika. Princes from all over the country were invited to participate.

Bhishma decided to attend the *swayamvar* on behalf of young Vichitravirya.

So Bhishma left for Kashi and entered King Kashya's court. All heads turned to see him. An old man stood up and said, 'What is Bhishma doing here? He has pledged never to marry. He cannot participate in the contest!'

This made Bhishma furious. He announced, 'I am here on behalf of King Vichitravirya. These three princesses will be his queens. I am taking them with me to Hastinapur!'

The court broke into chaos. Guards and princes came charging at Bhishma. Defeating everyone, Bhishma took away the three princesses and left in his chariot for Hastinapur.

Wedding preparations began in Vichitravirya's court. The entire kingdom was celebrating but princess Amba was very unhappy. She gathered courage and went to meet Bhishma and Satyavati in their chambers.

Bhishma and Satyavati were surprised to see her. Amba said, 'I have to tell you something very important. I am in love with King Shalva and want to marry him.'

Hearing this, Bhishma sent Amba back to Shalva. Reaching his palace, Amba ran towards Shalva and said, 'I have left Hastinapur to come back to you. Let's get married!'

But Shalva was furious. He said, 'Bhishma had taken you away forcefully. You must go back to him and marry him. I cannot accept you as my wife now.'

Amba returned to Hastinapur heartbroken. She went to Bhishma and told him what had happened when she went back to Shalva.

Bhishma was bound by his pledge to Dusharaj. He said, 'Princess, I am sorry but I cannot marry you or anybody else. I am Bhishma. I have vowed to never get married.'

This made Amba furious. She believed that Bhishma had spoilt her life. She wanted to take revenge. She went to many kingdoms asking for help but none of the kings agreed to fight the powerful Bhishma.

Finally, Amba prayed to Lord Shiva. Shiva heard her prayers and appeared before her. He gave her a boon. He said, 'One day, you will fight Bhishma and be the cause of his defeat.'

VYASA'S BOONS

Ambika and Ambalika married Vichitravirya and became his queens. Unfortunately, Vichitravirya died soon after his marriage. This left Hastinapur with no king.

Bhishma and Satyavati were worried. One evening, Bhishma went to Satyavati's chambers to meet her. He said, 'Dear Mother, I have a solution to our problems. Let us seek the help of your son Vyasa, the great sage.'

Long ago, when Satyavati was ferrying sage Parashara across the river, he noticed a foul smell around Satyavati. Impressed by Satyavati's dedication to her work, he said, "I am giving you the boon of sweet fragrance. The scent of flowers will surround you always. Also, a son named Vyasa, who will become the master of the vedas, will be born to you."

Vyasa was born with divine powers. He grew up quickly and left to live in the forest. Before leaving, Vyasa held Satyavati's hand and said, "Dear mother, I am leaving now but I promise that I will come to you whenever you seek my help."

Satyavati sent a messenger to invite Vyasa to the palace. Vyasa was very obedient and came immediately. Satyavati embraced him and said, 'Dear son, I have called you to help us in a difficult situation. The kingdom has no heir. I want you to bless Vichitravirya's wives with one son each.'

Vyasa sat in his chambers waiting for the queens. First, Ambika entered Vyasa's chambers. She saw Vyasa and shut her eyes in fright. Vyasa granted her the boon. Since Ambika's eyes were shut, her son was born blind. He was called Dhrithrashtra.

Next, Satyavati sent Ambalika to Vyasa's chambers. Ambalika was so scared that she turned pale with fright. As a result, she gave birth to a pale child who was named Pandu.

Satyavati was again unhappy. She went to Ambika and said, 'I have requested Vyasa to bless you with another son. You must go to his chambers to get the boon.'

Ambika was still scared of going to Vyasa. She thought for a while and decided to send her maid to receive Vyasa's boon. The maid fearlessly went up to Vyasa and greeted him with great devotion. Without seeing her, Vyasa blessed her with a son. The maid gave birth to a brave son, named Vidura.

In this way, Ambika and Ambalika had three sons. Since Dhrithrashtra was blind, Pandu became the King of Hastinapur while the wise Vidura became the prime minister. No one knew that Vidura's mother was a maid.

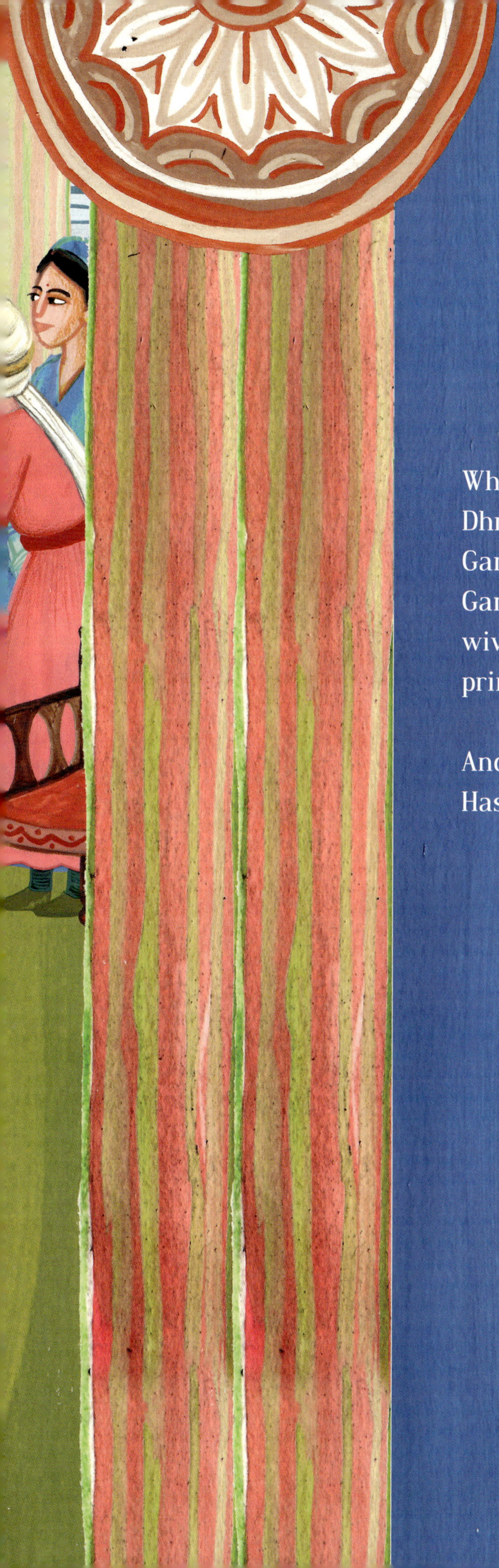

When the princes grew up, Dhrithrashtra married Gandhari, the princess of Gandhar. Pandu had two wives, princess Kunti and princess Madri.

And so the kingdom of Hastinapur continued to grow.

TITLES IN THIS SERIES

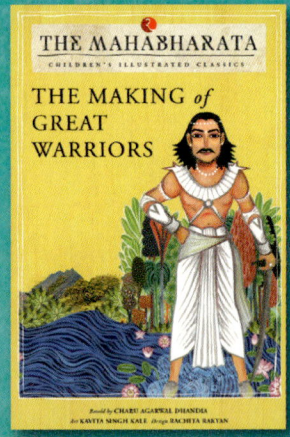
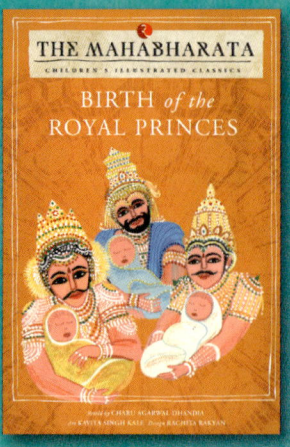
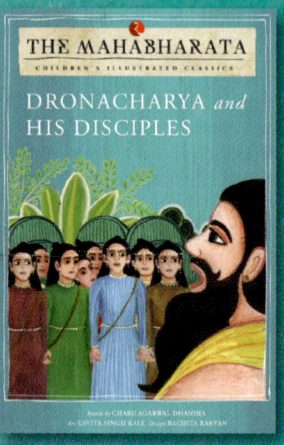
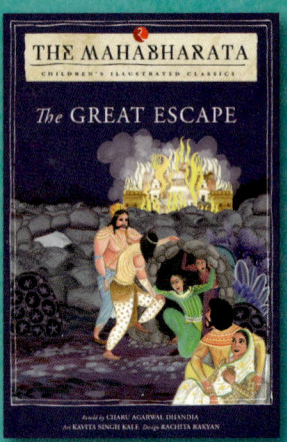
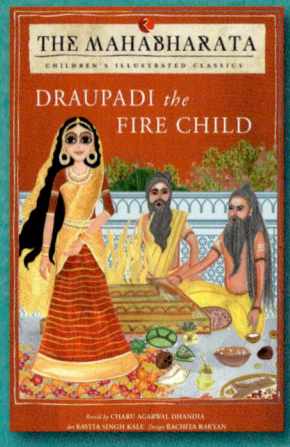
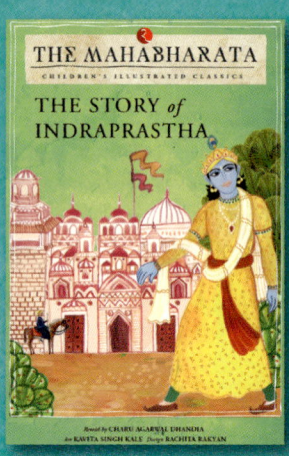
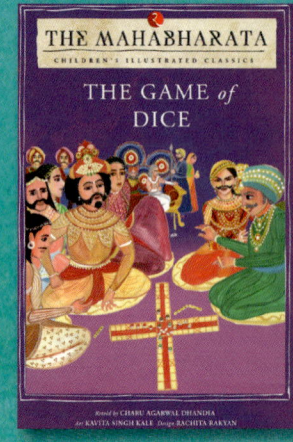
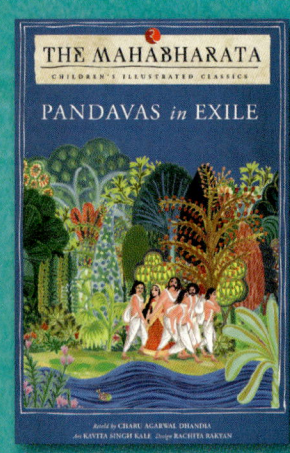
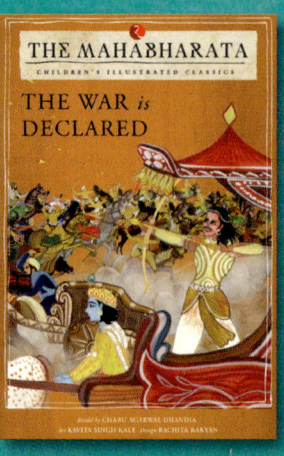